nickelodeon

PAW PATROL™

SHAPED COLOURING FUN

This book belongs to:

....

PAW PATROL™: SHAPED COLOURING FUN
A CENTUM BOOK 978-1-913865-01-6
Published in Great Britain by Centum Books Ltd
First published 2021
This edition published 2021
3 5 7 9 10 8 6 4 2

Centum Books Ltd, 20 Devon Square, Newton Abbot, Devon, TQ12 2HR, UK
books@centumbooksltd.co.uk
CENTUM BOOKS Limited Reg. No. 07641486
A CIP catalogue record for this book is available from the British Library.
Printed in China.

centum

"Whenever there's trouble, just yelp for help!"
says Ryder, leader of the PAW Patrol.

Rubble is going to build the biggest sandcastle ever!

"Ready for action," says Chase, the police pup.

No job is too big, no pup is too small!

"I'm all fired up," says Marshall, the fire pup.

Chase is returning the lost
baby geese to their mother.

"This pup's gotta fly!" says Skye, the pilot pup.

Chase is checking that work is going
well on Rubble's building site.

"Green means go!" says Rocky,
the recycling pup.

Who's ruff-ruff ready
for a beach emergency?

RUFF-RUFF READY!

"I can dig it," says Rubble, the builder pup.

Skye soars above Adventure Bay
to see who needs her help.

Let's dive in," says Zuma, the water-rescue pup.

There's trouble in Adventure Bay and Ryder knows Rubble is the pup for the job.

"Ice or snow, I'm ready to go!" says Everest, the mountain-rescue pup.

Zuma and Rocky know that friendship always comes first.

"I'm all ears!" says Tracker,
the jungle-rescue pup.

The PAW Patrol like to visit Katie's
Pet Parlour to get petted and pampered.

Katie's cute cat Cali loves to
eat and make mischief.

Chase is on the case in his
PAWsome police truck.

Rubble is a big softy when it comes to cute kitties.

The pups wear their camouflage
uniforms to help them hide.

Chase uses his spy training to be very quiet.

The PAW Patrol are on
an underwater mission.

When there are emergencies in the air,
just call the Air Patrol!

Splish, splash, splosh! Rubble is enjoying a bubble bath at the Pet Parlour.

Whenever you're in trouble,
just yelp for help!.

Rubble is ready to dig in to his dog bowl!

Mayor Goodway thanks the PAW Patrol pups for saving the day!

Ryder hands out treats to the pups for doing a PAWsome job.

The PAW Patrol is always ready for action and adventure!